BEATING CANCER

One Truth at a Time

What You Believe Determines Your Journey

For Newly Diagnosed Patients

Marianne C. McDonough

Sapphire River Publishing Services, LLC
7101 York Avenue South
Suite 343
Minneapolis, MN 55435

Typesetting & Design by Selah Media Group

Cover Images
Stepping Stones: © travellinglight | Getty Images/iStock Collection
Eagle: © Jganz | Getty Images/iStock Collection

ISBN-13: 978-0-9966977-3-6
LCCN: 2018911352

Printed in the United States of America

Contents

Acknowledgments v

Introduction 1

Keeping It Simple: How to Use and Enjoy this Guide 3

When Eagles Fly 9

1. Choose What to Believe.. 11
    Cancer Lies to Us—What You Believe Determines Your Journey

2. Find Bridges and Boundaries... 25
    Connect with Others—You Are Not Alone

3. Strategize Your Treatment... 39
    Prepare and Decide—It's Your Journey

4. Settle Faith and Mortality Issues 55
    Cancer Requires an Answer—What Do You Really Believe?

5. Gear Up for Treatment... 67
    Focus—Give It All You've Got

6. Conquer Stress 79
    Stress Is a Heavy Weight—Lift, Press, and Release

7. Plan Your Future 93
    Survivorship—Be Cancer Smart

Appendix.. 107

Acknowledgments

Sometimes books happen in their own way at their own time. This one began at my five-year anniversary physical when my oncologist, Dr. Rachel Lerner, suggested that the components of my first book would work well for support groups. As a result, I began to write a companion guide for *8 Steps to Getting Real with Cancer.* Much to my surprise though, when I finished, I had written a new book. Basically, the text was almost entirely different, and I had added research information and a number of new concepts to those of *8 Steps.* Thus, with gratitude I acknowledge Dr. Rachel Lerner for the idea, hoping she likes the new book equally as well.

Thank you, as always, to my family and friends for their confidence in my calling to write.

Thank you to my faithful critique group members who so patiently read and reread the contents that evolved. Their love and prayers constantly encouraged me.

Thank you to the readers of *8 Steps* whose positive feedback spurred me to attempt yet another cancer book for newly diagnosed patients.

Finally, thank you to all the generous and skilled writing teachers and editors who have influenced my work and encouraged me, especially my advisor, Professor Emeritus Hazel Dicken Garcia from the University of Minnesota. Few people have believed in me more than she, and no one else taught me more.

I am blessed.

— Marianne C. McDonough

Introduction

What follows here is a simple path for a complicated journey. Cancer is like stepping into the cockpit of a commercial airbus, sitting down at the controls, and wondering what all those strange buttons do. At first you don't even know the destination much less the timing. You have no idea how to fly the plane at all, but here you are, a pilot learning how to do something you never wanted to learn.

Moreover, you feel as though you have already crashed.

Obviously, I'm not much at sugarcoating the cancer process, but I am a strong proponent of mastering it. I believe the best way to do that is one truth at a time. As you journey through this book, I hope you will attack cancer with a dedicated vengeance and more determination and courage than you ever thought possible.

What do you believe about cancer? More importantly, what do you believe about cancer in your own body, life, and future?

Cancer has a well-deserved reputation. You may not know much about it, but you've heard enough to be upset and shocked. What lies ahead for you?

You are entering one of the hardest phases of cancer right now. The diagnosis and treatment periods are notoriously intense, sometimes confusing, and always life altering.

Just know there are lots of survivors and other champions out there cheering you on. We know how life changing it is to get to the victory side of this battle.

You can do this.

Keeping It Simple

How to Use and Enjoy This Guide

I'm going to keep this as simple as possible, and I suggest you do the same. I remember how stressed I was during the first month following my diagnosis, especially with the myriad of data I had to figure out.

When I was newly diagnosed, I wanted a small, practical, quick-read book that could help me figure out how to put one step in front of the other. What I found were heavy, philosophical works that didn't appeal to my worn-out and exhausted brain. Appointments and researching crammed my days, and an overwhelming to-do list interrupted my sleep. Sound familiar?

This is a guide and resource that you can use however you want. What matters is that you seek your own truths your own way, because that is how you will find power and clarity for the days ahead.

People who haven't been where you are might suggest you set aside a daily time slot for this process, but I know better. Things don't always work like that with cancer. So I designed this book to work well in short increments or long. You can give it as much time or as little as needed, and feel free to write in it or highlight text.

Divided into seven chapters, this guide topically coordinates with my first book, *8 Steps to Getting Real with Cancer*, but the format as well as much of the text differs, especially in focus. *8 Steps* combines my story with information for both patients and those who love them. *Beating Cancer* exclusively addresses you, the patient.

Additionally, I created *Beating Cancer* for personal reflection and/or group discussion. I ask pertinent questions you can simply read, or you can journal your answers if that appeals to you. Short spaces are available for your convenience. Understand you don't have to worry about grammar, length, or appearance.

If you choose to journal and make notes, I hope this book will serve as a treasured memorial of the raw thoughts, revelations, challenges, and victories of your cancer journey. On your survivorship anniversaries, you could review it to see how far you've come. I want you to be proud of this time in your life—the way you conducted your treatment period and how you surmounted the rugged terrain of this incredibly harsh disease.

Each chapter contains four sections:

Truths to Free You

The first step in your journey is to discover your own beliefs about yourself and cancer. To help you do that, I will present some of the myths surrounding cancer in the culture. You may be surprised how many you've incorporated into your belief system. My goal is to encourage you to clarify your own truths, know that cancer does not own you or your life, and find peace and confidence in the process. Then you will articulate your own truths— not mine, but yours. This is your journey. I want you to discover your own reservoir of strength, faith, and values.

If you've read *8 Steps*, you will notice that I chose different myths for *Beating Cancer* in order to be more specific and applicable to patients.

Truths to Empower You

Cancer is a bully that attempts to hijack us. It's as though it helps itself to the driver's seat of our lives and pompously declares, "I'm taking over. From now on I'm telling you where you're going, for how long, and what you'll be doing in the meantime." The fact is that your life belongs to you. You belong in the driver's seat. It's your car, so take the wheel. Cancer doesn't have the right to drive your car. No matter what stage you're in, you do not belong in the back seat of your own car.

Does cancer affect the course of your life? Yes, there's no way around that. Change, especially as a by-product of crisis, happens to all of us. We don't always get to choose whether or not change will occur. We do, however, have the right to choose what to believe and do with the process.

Are you going to change? From my experience and reports of others, I don't know how you can avoid it. Of course, some changes are extremely hard, maybe even negative, while others are beneficial in ways we can't imagine at diagnosis. By the time I entered survivorship, I had decided that change was only a choice away from opportunity. The operative word is "choice," and choices are based on what you believe. Do you see the pattern here? Deliberate, active choice-making skills based on well-formulated beliefs will empower your journey.

Truths to Inspire You

If ever there's a time to be inspired, it's when you battle a life-threatening illness. Inspiration fosters the power team of hope and vision. Without hope, how can anyone face cancer? But hope does not exist without vision and vice versa. In fact, hope cradles vision, providing a safe place for it to land. Vision, for its part, gives purpose to hope.

Of course, the sting of your diagnosis is still fresh, and you might ask, "What's the point of a vision? My world has collapsed, and my imagination has other things to consider." But that is exactly the point. Your imagination will envision something, one way or the other. Why not feed it a positive outcome that you can believe in and fight for?

Whatever happens, the onset of cancer may be the most fragile time of your journey. Now is the time to strengthen your resolve. Look beyond the diagnosis and find faith and hope for the future.

Truths to Discover

As an additional and optional journaling exercise, in this section I offer thoughts for sensory expression or relaxation. The goal is to engage your imagination. Up to this point, you will have recorded thoughts, but imagining is different from thinking. Imagination flows without structure and reveals interesting insights that often elude the rational process.

You don't have to be a musician or artist or have any particular talent to engage in this section. You might simply choose to find music that relaxes or inspires you. I will offer various suggestions for art, free-associative process, or whatever appeals to you.

For example, I will present an image that's significant to me with a brief description and reason. I didn't draw it. I found it online and enjoyed the process. I encourage you to respond to my image, draw if you want to, or insert graphics such as drawings or photographs that mean something to you.

Sometimes our senses help us interpret life while our brains try to catch up, moving past reason to revelation.

Choices for the Journey and New Mindsets

At the end of each chapter, you will see two short sections—Choices for the Journey and New Mindsets.

Choices for the Journey are one-sentence action points. The intent is to make a plan, even if it's a small one. Through all the disappointments and crises of life, I've learned making a plan—even a small one—changes the course of events. No matter the difficulty or size, one step gives you at least a glimpse of hope. Even a mere glimpse is like the first streams of sunrise promising a new day. As you watch, you know the full force of solar power is not far behind.

Choices for the Journey will also recap the chapter themes. Use them as ideas to activate your truths in practical and specific ways. Truths are not knickknacks for our mental curio shelves. They're the tools we need for everyday life.

New Mindsets offer you the opportunity to select a statement, concept, or truth (from my writing or yours) that was the most significant to you in the chapter. Then summarize it in one sentence as a simple take-away thought.

Finally, before you begin this book, I want to emphasize two things:

1. I am not trying to tell you how to think, what to believe, or what to do. Rather my intent is to help you clarify and explore your own values.
2. I am adamant about your empowerment. You are in charge of your own journey. It belongs to you and no one else. This book is not about me. Rather it describes a process through which you can find freedom and strength to fight cancer on your own terms and win.

Beating cancer doesn't happen by accident or default. You don't often stumble upon truth, but you can frequently stumble without it. Truth is a treasure you actively seek. Passivity thrives on lies and opens the door to depression. Don't even touch the knob on that door.

That said, let's do this.

When Eagles Fly

I love to watch eagles fly.
Sometimes they glide as though air were made of silk.
Sometimes they power up as though air were
a mountain to be mastered.
And sometimes they dive and swerve
as though surfing the currents.

But nothing compares to eagles flying in a storm
above tumultuous waters.
When waves with angry fists pound against the rocks,
when all the other birds have taken shelter,
when blustery horizons bode dark shadows,
then eagles rise, stretch their mighty wings,
attack the skies, and ride the wind.

It's as though they say to themselves, "I have the wings for this."

They know they can handle the fierceness,
so much so that they fly directly into it,
face on, courageous, and strong.
Eagles can teach us about storms.
When cancer pounds against us,
when we feel alone,
when it's time to confront the storm,
ride the wind, and own the sky,
we can say to ourselves,
"I have the wings for this."

9

You don't often stumble upon truth,
but you can stumble without it.

Chapter One

Choose What to Believe

Cancer Lies to Us—What You Believe Determines Your Journey

Truths to Free You

Whether you are a fan or a critic of reality TV, you have a lot of company. Critics say all reality TV shows are contrived. Fans say of course they're contrived, some more than others, but who cares? Most of us, however, agree that we crave truth in our real lives, especially in times of crisis such as trauma or illness.

Let's begin with basic questions: What does truth have to do with cancer? More specifically, what does truth have to do with freedom in the cancer journey?

First, we need to establish what we think about cancer. We can use some formal definitions to start. But to fight this deplorable disease, we must decide for ourselves what we believe about it.

Dictionaries refer to cancers as tumors from uncontrolled division of body cells. The Oxford Encyclopedic Dictionary adds that cancer is often used as a metaphor for things that are "evil or destructive" and "hard to contain or eradicate."[1] Most of us can affirm those descriptions.

Cancer is not a singular disease. In fact, the National Cancer Institute says there are more than one hundred types of cancer, usually named for the organs or tissues of origination. What differentiates them is how they grow and spread.

One way to discover our truths about cancer is to identify cultural myths that surround it. Myths can seem nebulous, partially wrong, or even totally wrong. In any case, like sour milk, a myth may look good, but when you taste it, it's bitter and unhealthy to ingest. The Merriam Webster Dictionary describes a myth as "an unfounded or false notion." As you examine the myths presented in this book, find the unfounded or false notions, see if you have believed some or all of them, and then write what you believe to be true.

Myth #1: Cancer is so complicated and powerful, we are helpless against it.

If I believed this myth, I wouldn't have written this book.

A. What were your thoughts at the time of diagnosis? Those thoughts will give you clues about your initial definitions of and beliefs about cancer. Do not overthink or filter. Just write. Understand you will change, grow, and develop that definition as you read through this book. Your answers here are merely a starting point.

At first, cancer tries to fill us with doubt and confusion. What did I do wrong? Why is this happening? Why me? The pressure to despair looms like dark skies bundling hail and thunder into a raging storm. We know what's coming. The air is thick with foreboding.

If we ignore the ominous clouds of cancer, we will surely experience the worst of the storm. Instead we read the skies, prepare, don protective apparel, and find shelter.

How do we do that?

Not surprisingly, through our life experiences, we assimilate and acquire convictions about everything. You already have well-developed beliefs within your own brain and soul. That's a good thing unless those beliefs hinder your resolve to beat cancer. To ensure you're on track, as hard as it is, you are wise to seek clarity, change what needs to change, and articulate truths that are accurate and helpful.

It's tempting to dismiss our inner thoughts during crises. We wonder, "Can't I just put my mental struggles aside while I'm fighting this disease? Don't I have enough to do, for heaven's sake, without delving into a bunch of self-reflection?" Of course, the answer to that is yes. As a survivor, though, I want to share two things that are rarely discussed. Your beliefs and emotions intermingle in cancer in powerful ways, and when we ignore our inner struggles, sooner or later our emotions will emerge. In fact, many people experience sadness, even ongoing depression, after cancer treatment.

In my follow-up instructions from my oncology clinic, one paragraph stood out like neon lights on a marquee:

> *As treatment ends, people start to feel better physically. But, ending treatment can trigger a rush of emotions, ranging from excitement and celebration to anger and sadness. This emotional change happens because cancer survivors often relax their guard and process all the feelings they put aside during treatment. . . . For many people, this change leads to two to three months of emotional ups and downs.*

Recently I heard a breast cancer survivor describe her six months of post-treatment depression. I felt compassion for her and do not fault people who experience negative emotions or seasons in life, much less after battling cancer. But if we can find ways to avoid the ups and downs and approach survivorship feeling peaceful and stable, surely that is the preferred path.

The National Cancer Institute says, "People have found that when they express strong feelings like anger or sadness, they're more able to let go of them. Some sort out their feelings by talking to friends or family, other cancer survivors, a support group, or a counselor. But even if you prefer not to discuss your cancer with others, you can still sort out your feelings by thinking about them or writing them down."[2]

That's exactly what we're doing in this book. In remaining chapters we'll discuss how we share with others.

Myth #2: Inner reflection is unnecessary and a waste of time.

Myth #3: I might fall apart or get too emotional, and that would be embarrassing.

B. Examine Myths #2 and #3.
1. What tenets are at the basis of these myths?

2. How would you rate yourself in being truthful with yourself? Always? Mostly? Frequently? Sometimes? Rarely?

3. How would you rate yourself in being truthful with others? Always? Mostly? Frequently? Sometimes? Rarely?

4. What is your attitude toward self-reflection? What are the potential benefits? What are the potential challenges?

C. When you read the myths in these chapters, you will have space to respond by writing your own truths or values that counter the myths. In the appendix, I list mine for reference. But I suggest you write yours first. What are your Truths #1, #2, and #3?

Truths to Empower You

Even though you may not feel heroic, you are already a cancer hero or heroine. You just took the hard blow of diagnosis, and here you are, ready for the fight and moving forward. If you are facing a reoccurrence of your cancer, you are doubly heroic. Sometimes cancer patients find it hard to accept such a compliment because they don't believe they deserve it. But understand that by virtue of your commitment to defeat cancer, you are worthy. The diagnostic/treatment season is a rocky road to walk. In time, as we journey together through this guide, fear will bow to determination, and cancer will lose its bravado.

What do you respect about the way you have handled things so far? If there's something you wish you had done or had not done, chalk it up to experience and let go of whatever it is. This is cancer. Have you done this or even anything like it before? Maybe someday, with the benefit of your hard-earned experience, you can help someone else.

Courage often occurs in defining moments you never thought would happen, such as the first chemo or radiation treatment. Isn't it interesting that we so often use the phrase "take courage"? If courage is something we take, where do we find it?

At the onset of my cancer, my husband, Tom, wanted somehow to be my hero, but he couldn't rescue me, fight the enemy for me, or spare me any part of the experience. Rather, what I really needed from him was respect and assurance that I could fight and win. Did I want support? Of course I did, but cancer seemed to have robbed my personal power, and I decided it was my responsibility to take it back where it belonged—in me. That required courage. I found it by believing I was worth the fight. Acknowledging my own value gave me confidence to tackle the daily and surprising challenges of cancer. What I believed about my life and my prospects to beat cancer drew a line that cancer could not cross. My truth belonged to me. It was within my being and the heartbeat of my identity.

Myth #4: I will never be strong or healthy again.

D. What is your attitude toward the cancer in your body? Are you afraid of it?

I've often spoken about the anger I felt and still do feel toward cancer. But I believe that justified anger is empowering. Are you angry? If you are, can you think of ways that you can make that anger work to your advantage against cancer?

E. Write your own counteracting truths to Myth #4.

Truths to Inspire You

The following is from one of my blogs:

Cancer is a dream stealer.

We all have dreams, but when something threatens our longevity, we wonder if we should even bother.

I'm saying to you today: Go ahead and "bother."

Dreams represent what we believe to be possible.
Dreams refresh our enthusiasm to forge the future.
Dreams reveal who we really are.
Dreams renew our capacity to imagine and create.

This is not the time to let despair bury a perfectly good dream.

Hold on!

Dreams give oxygen to hope.
Dreams give breath to vision.
Dreams give purpose to healing.[3]

Think of dreaming as a ladder. The initial rung bids us to view what's at the top, reach for something we can't obtain any other way than to climb, and take the first step. Remember what I said about hope? How important it is to your journey, healing, and recovery? It's never too early to dream. I'm not talking about going into denial or dreaming some trumped-up fantasy. That's not dreaming. Nor is it even remotely healthy. Rather I'm encouraging you to take time to breathe, rest, and let your heart look beyond the immediate crisis for a reason to fight for your future.

As a survivor, I assure you that hope is your best friend and cancer's worst nightmare.

So what's at the top of the ladder for you?

F.   List what you envision at the top of your ladder and copy those items onto an index card so you can easily display it or use it as a bookmark in your current reading.

Myth #5: Cancer is an automatic death sentence. Why dream for a future that will never happen?

G.   Many people still believe this misconception despite all the evidence to the contrary. From my perspective, it's immeasurably offensive to us survivors who have fought so hard for our lives. What do you believe?

Truths to Discover

Do you have a favorite place? Somewhere that brings contentment and refreshes you? For me, it's a park near my apartment. I love to walk through the landscaped paths, sit or read on a bench, watch people, and rest. I feel free, energized, and peaceful there. For my husband, his favorite place is his boat where he fishes every chance he gets. What is your favorite resting spot? How does it make you feel and why? Imagine being there now. Draw, describe, or represent that place.

Through this exercise, you may discover core elements of life that are most important to you and things you need for the days ahead during treatment. Articulating those values helps you prioritize.

Choices for Your Journey—Make a Plan

The following choices are time-specific suggestions, but select only what appeals to you, or write your own in any order you prefer.

Today: I will take time to reflect on my beliefs about cancer.

This week: I will identify and acknowledge my concerns about cancer.

This month: I will take courage for the cancer journey by respecting who I am and the value of my own life.

Long term: Someday I will gladly listen to and encourage a new cancer patient.

New Mindset Regarding Cancer

Summarize your most significant take-away concept from this chapter.

Meditation

Take time to imagine, relax, and rest. Feel free to write your thoughts as they come to you.

Possible free-association words:

- Diagnosis
- Power
- Journey

*Even though it may not take a village,
someone in the village might help you in
ways you wouldn't have imagined.*

Chapter Two

Find Bridges and Boundaries

Connect with Others—
You Are Not Alone

Truths to Free You

Sometimes songs do a great job of helping us describe life situations.

Do you remember the song "Bridge Over Troubled Water"? The premise is that we can offer loved ones safe footing in times of extreme sorrow. A bridge metaphor certainly applies to our loved ones and supporters in many ways:

- Bridges connect us from where we are to where we want to go.
- Bridges are solid, reliable, and immovable.
- Bridges cannot protect people from storms but they can protect them from drowning.
- Bridges resist corrosion and stand the test of time.

Throughout my own treatment, I remember well the troubled waters, but I also recall the unselfish support of good people in my life. My daughter Shannon said she would do anything to help, that her busy attorney career would not deter her. My other daughter Sheila created a website for me and served as a contact person for friends. Tom took me out to dinner and provided a sounding board for thoughts. I still have the handmade get-well cards from my grandchildren. Add to that numerous acts of kindness from relatives, friends, and neighbors.

All of those people were bridges for me, understanding also that sometimes I had to swim through those turbulent waters and face the pounding waves myself. That's when boundaries applied. During those moments, I had to accept that it was primarily my storm. It was up to me to decide when, how much, and how often I leaned on people. Boundary times included my final decisions on treatment, finding personal meditation time and space, and preparing myself well for doctors' visits. Those activities along with their foundational mindsets benefitted my journey, because making my own choices and planning wisely empowered me.

You will need both bridges and boundaries in the days ahead.

Myth #6: I don't want to burden or impose on anyone.

The American Cancer Society website cites a "Coping Checklist for Patients" in which it includes the following as a healthy coping method: "I talk with others and share my concerns when I face a problem."[4] Conversely, in its list of unhelpful coping methods, it says, "I wish people would leave me alone."[5]

That doesn't mean patients can't or shouldn't take time to think and reflect. What it means is that ongoing withdrawal and isolation do not help. In fact, those mechanisms could very well disempower and sabotage your healing.

A. Consider the tasks of informing and interacting with your priority relationships, including such things as degree of difficulty, approach, setting, timing, boundaries, and answering the question, "How can I help?"

1. Your spouse or other significant peer relationships

2. Your children

3. Your parents, siblings, and other relatives

4. Your friends, neighbors, co-workers, or any other supporters

Recently, I heard a young man speak who had cancer as a teenager. Fighting tears, he said, "I felt like I was bringing my family down." I could relate, although I surmised his family would have gladly done anything possible to help him. How I wished I could have spared my own family! But realistically we were in it together, and that's just the way it was.

From another perspective, a man about twenty-five years old shared with me that, when he was a teenager, his mother did not tell him she had cancer. Someone else in the family broke the news, but neither she nor anyone else shared much about her journey. Wounded and feeling like an outsider, he avoided everyone, leaving the house whenever he could. When I met him, he was still dealing with the guilt and sadness of that experience. I defended her right to determine her own path, suggesting that she may have been trying to protect him. But I also told him I believe patients do well to tell their children the truth, adjusting for age and maturity level as needed.

Some readers of *8 Steps* have shared great tips with me. For example, one person told me that children of cancer patients benefit from the objective viewpoint and assistance of a trustworthy adult outside the immediate family unit. Whether a relative, minister, friend, school counselor, or professional therapist, such a person provides a listening ear and wisdom that fosters both short-term and long-term support.

Myth #7: I have to protect my family and loved ones from the truth about what I'm really feeling and going through.

    B. Is there anyone about whom you are especially concerned or worried? What effect do you think your worry, anxiety, or guilt will have on your healing?

    C. The priority goal for all involved—you and your supporters—is that you beat this disease and get well. How does Myth #7 possibly sabotage that goal?

After I told Tom I had cancer, his well-meaning re-action was to share what he thought I should do. Then, thankfully, a friend whose wife went through treatment told him that I needed to make my own decisions. At the time I appreciated that wisdom, but today I applaud it. Support is crucial but not at the expense of the patient's autonomy and confidence.

During life's struggles, all of us choose whether we're going to handle them alone or involve someone else. Frankly, on occasion I've chosen the former route for certain situations but not with cancer. It's not a going-it-alone situation. That, however, doesn't mean others can take it over or lead it for you. You are in charge.

D. Write your own Truths #6 and #7.

Truths to Empower You

When I first heard my diagnosis, I was home after wait-ing five days for the biopsy results. The statement "you have invasive ductile carcinoma" was bad enough, but the cancer to-do list that followed landed on me like a truck jackknifed in an ice storm. I literally dropped to the floor. As I lay there processing the news, I began to clench my fists. When I stood up, I knew I had entered a cancer war zone.

War is an apt metaphor for cancer. Since you and

I are on the inside of the cancer world, we know the reality of what we're facing. I'm a veteran on the victory side, and you have just been called to the front lines. It's not a geographically distant war, because it's lodged within your own body. This is as close to home as it gets.

Considering the war analogy, I propose that we all need fellow soldiers. Do you want to be in this particular foxhole all by yourself? I assure you that I did not. At this point, you might ask, "Isn't my family enough?" If that's true for you, of course the answer is yes. Even though it may not take a village, someone in the village might help you in ways you wouldn't have imagined. Additionally, sometimes families are broken, weakened from other traumas or situations, and unable to help for some reason. Or maybe they're estranged from you. If that describes your family, check your own instincts for what's best for you.

Before we go further with the war analogy, let's clarify one thing. I cringe when I hear people say that someone "lost her battle with cancer." I think that is grossly unfair. Anyone who has battled cancer at all is a winner for standing up against it. Moreover, all of us, whether current patient or survivor, have won every battle we can with what we've had at our disposal in the here and now of contemporary science and treatment. Additionally, our valor and experience contribute to that science for those who will be diagnosed after us.

So go ahead and treat cancer like war, win every battle possible, and trek your way toward survivorship, understanding that no one can take the dignity of your brave journey away from you.

E. What parts of the cancer process resemble war?

F. How can people best help you right now? How will you communicate with your support team? Directly? Internet? Delegate a contact person? My older daughter offered to make my website for me and became my contact person.

Myth #8: I can't make my own decisions. What if I'm wrong?

When I deliberated about treatment options, I talked things through with a few trusted people from whom I welcomed thoughtful feedback, insights, and observations, but I set a mental boundary. I generally didn't ask for opinions or advice, because I wondered what would happen if I chose something they didn't recommend or agree with. I was concerned that some other awkward relationship issue might even evolve.

As for right or wrong cancer treatment protocols, I sympathize with your dilemma. The stakes are high. I've been there, and we'll talk more about that in chapters three and five. For now, understand there is much controversy and disagreement among the general populace and health care professionals. When the time comes to select treatment, however, the reality is you will still have to say yes or no. One of the purposes of this book is to help you walk that part of the journey with as much confidence as possible. Your final decisions are the ones that make the most sense at the time—the ones you've chosen using the tools, information, and most competent professional advice you can find.

G. What boundaries will you set and why? For example, what don't you want to share with people? Or are you uncomfortable sharing certain details with some people but not others? Whose feedback will you welcome?

H. Write your own counteracting truth to Myth #8.

Truths to Inspire You
Your vision of the future gives your mental binoculars a destination to view.

So how do we acquire an honest and inspiring vision? Let's begin with some possible and practical tips:

- Spend time with your favorite people. Talk. Reflect. Learn. Love. Receive love.
- Journal, using the exercises here, both written and art based, or additional journaling and reflection of your choice. You will be surprised at the clarity you will achieve.
- Reread a favorite inspirational book or find a new one, something you can absorb in small daily increments.
- Reach out to a survivor you respect and ask what worked well for him or her.
- Make a playlist of music to comfort and inspire you.
- Search the internet for cancer support websites that provide good wisdom and insights you can adopt into your own mindset.
- Do you like movies? Why not treat yourself to an inspiring, feel-good movie?
- Find a support group.
- Make time to seek counsel with someone who extends compassion and positive wisdom.

Vision building is like planning a garden. Every plant is positioned for maximum success and its contribution to the whole. The annual ones bloom constantly but have to be replanted the next season. Perennials, on the other hand, may not bloom as often, but once they're planted, they provide a reliable foundation.

Applying this analogy, you need visions for the immediate treatment season as well as others to take root for the rest of your lifetime.

Don't work too hard at this. The key is to energize hope for your future, not wear yourself out. Here are four criteria: keep your visions simple, achievable, stress free, and satisfying.

I.   What are your short-term hopes for cancer treatment?

J.   What are your long-term hopes for survivorship?

K.   How can your loved ones help you in the days ahead? What will you ask of them?

L.   What will you do when your treatment ends? Something special with your family? Or your friends? My husband, Tom, and I already had a family trip planned for the summer after I completed my treatments. The timing was perfect for me to initiate my survivorship on a positive note.

Truths to Discover

How can your bridges connect you from where you are to where you want to be?

Choices for the Journey—Make a Plan

The following choices are time-specific suggestions, but select only what appeals to you, or write your own in any order you prefer.

Today: I will write a list of decisions to make in the next few weeks.

This week: I will ask someone for help when I need it.

This month: I will listen to people I trust and respect.

But I will not expect or allow them to take over or make decisions for me.

Long term: I will give myself permission to dream for a positive future.

New Mindset for Sharing My Journey

Summarize your most significant take-away concept from this chapter.

Meditation

Take time to imagine, relax, and rest. Feel free to write your thoughts as they come to you.

Possible free-association words:
- Friends
- Safety
- Confidence

Eagles can teach us about storms.
When cancer pounds against us,
When we feel alone,
When it's time to confront the storm,
ride the wind, and own the sky.[6]

Marianne McDonough

Chapter Three

Strategize Your Treatment

Prepare and Decide—
It's Your Journey

Truths to Free You

Obstacles abound in life, right? They vary in degree, origin, and nature, but some obstacles are internal and harder to admit. For example, before cancer I knew that I tended toward perfectionism, so I made sure I didn't expect myself to be the model patient. That meant I would allow myself to be human and not worry about doing everything right or embarrassing myself in front of doctors or other medical professionals.

What is your attitude toward doctors?

Many of us view them as qualified allies in the fight against disease. But there are people who see them as intimidating or unapproachable. The result is that some patients either avoid medical care or become passive and minimally involved in their treatment planning. In any case, cancer requires a verdict on these issues, because our beliefs about medical providers will help or hinder our cancer journey.

Before we go any further, understand it's important to accommodate your own personality as well as your beliefs. I was intensely involved and proactive. I've known others, however, who felt hesitant to take that approach. To those patients, I say to you if you don't want to know everything, you don't have to know everything. But I suggest you learn at least enough to confirm and adopt your doctors' recommendations with confidence that you are taking the best possible path.

Remember, it's your journey. No one else can live it for you. And I believe you are the best one to lead it in the way that suits and fits you.

Here are some reasons to clarify your beliefs about doctors and medical treatment:

- To be an effective patient for your own welfare, you must ask questions until you are satisfied with the answers.
- If you are totally passive, you will undermine your own healing by not communicating what you want, believe, or need.
- Passivity reinforces the powerlessness that the cancer diagnosis started.
- Rapport with your doctor will help you get the best care for yourself. Your ability to relate and connect with each other will establish mutual respect and an ability to work as a team.
- Shame and embarrassment don't belong in the cancer journey and are of no help whatsoever.

In its online Healthy Headlines article "Why It's Important to Be Honest with Your Doctor," Novanthealth. org quotes Dr. Jarrod Sheatsley. He says, "Often patients feel that physicians are talking down to them or talking over their heads. Unfortunately, if they don't tell us, we don't realize that they don't understand what we're saying. The best thing a patient can do is take an active role in their health care."[7] Dr. Sheatsley further notes that sometimes patients leave out information such as certain symptoms because they're embarrassed, or they surmise the symptoms are unimportant. When that happens, he says it can lead to "less-than-optimum care or even have harmful consequences."[8]

Thankfully, I believe that my oncology center provided optimum care for me. But I was also aware that I couldn't expect doctors and nurses to be perfect either. Thus, I spoke up when applicable, sought answers, and made changes when necessary, even asking for a different doctor at one point. The radiation oncologist assigned to me was obviously competent, but I didn't feel we communicated well. I had not experienced that issue with my primary oncologist and surgeon.

I suggest you search for the team that fits you best. One of my friends opted to use doctors from different clinics, gleaning their names by recommendation from her friends. Another friend consulted doctors in several clinics, evaluating all, and then selecting the clinical team with the approach that made the most sense to him. In any case, how you choose and relate to your medical team is one of the most important decisions you'll ever make.

Myth #9: I'm better off keeping my thoughts to myself and doing what I'm told.

Again, I acknowledge that some of you feel overwhelmed by all the data and complexities of cancer, especially as a new patient. I understand. The magnitude of what has happened to you worries you, and you feel drained already. Here's the reality, though. There will come a moment when you decide on treatments and sign consent papers. Ultimately, you will own your final decisions.

For that reason, among others already discussed, I agree with Dr. Sheatsley about taking an active role. Although I encourage you to know your own limits and be kind to yourself, the decisions will ultimately belong to you. Learn what you can, ask questions that at least cover the basics, and seek help with the rest of it without relinquishing your own power to approve and choose.

Then go forward and persevere with every ounce of strength you have.

A. What expectations do you typically place on yourself as a patient?

B. Make your own list of traits of an effective, responsible patient.

C. I think doctors are a little like churches. The reason we have so many kinds and types is that patients differ in taste, personality, and needs. With that in mind, list attributes that you would prefer to find in a doctor/provider. For example: business-like, communicative, compassionate, efficient, and so on.

Regarding cancer patients you've known, you've probably heard or said something like, "She's doing great. She never complains and always has a smile on her face."

43

Since we're focusing on truth here, now that you're a cancer patient, don't you think that's a tall order for such a nasty disease? I'm not suggesting you should go around complaining or with a frown on your face. But I want to relieve you of the unrealistic and unfair expectation that you have to put on a facade in front of people, and that includes your doctors.

Myth #10: I have to be strong and keep my composure all the time.

D. Write your own Truths #9 and #10.

Truths to Empower You

Since I knew next to nothing about cancer when I was diagnosed, I was shocked by how much I needed to learn within a few short weeks. Perhaps that's the case with you as well. Understandably, clinics expect people to make decisions as quickly as possible—not necessarily to apply pressure, but to expedite treatment.

The first month you deal with cancer puts your brain on high alert. Have you ever tried to drive in a foreign country on the other side of the road with no idea how to read the signs? Cancer is like that. Ordinarily, you might be a good driver, but when the rules of the road are foreign to you, you must adjust and consider every detail. With so many questions bombarding your mind, you hardly know where to begin. Normally I'm a fairly right-brained person, but I can kick my left brain into gear when necessary. And with cancer, it was definitely necessary, especially to wade through all the data. Moreover, when I met my doctors, I wanted to be informed enough to take advantage of my time with them not only to get answers but also to dialogue about options and how things would happen.

Thanks to that experience, I can now suggest some research tips for you:

- Search the internet cautiously. Although it can help in many ways, it can also terrify. And it isn't always correct. Substantiate your internet information through other sources as well.
- Go to the library or a bookstore.
- Keep a notebook. I used a three-ring binder with subject dividers.
- Search your oncology department for pamphlets and booklets. Mine had excellent materials in the lobby/waiting area.
- Take advantage of classes offered by your clinic or community.
- Talk to a friend or a friend of a friend, but by all means become informed. Select these people wisely, though. If someone is negative or fatalistic, move on and find another comrade who exudes faith and hope.

When you've gathered the information you want, you'll need help to decipher, interpret, combine, and select data correctly to determine what pertains to you and your diagnosis in practical terms. It's like buying a kit to make a model car. Just because you have all the pieces doesn't mean you know how to put it together. You're still in charge. But to choose and execute the best treatment regimen, you're wise to find consultants and doctors you respect with expertise you trust.

> E. Here are some basic questions described by the MD Anderson Cancer Center:
> - What type of cancer do I have? What is my exact diagnosis?
> - Where is the cancer located? Has it spread?
> - What's the stage of my cancer? What is my prognosis?
> - What are my treatment options? Which do you recommend and why?
> - What are possible risks and side effects?
> - Are clinical trials an option for me?
> - How will treatment affect my daily life?
> - What can I do to stay as healthy as possible before, during, and after treatment?
> - What support services are available?[9]

Here are some questions one of my readers suggested to me.
- What tests are needed?
- What will you find out?
- How will the results help me as a patient?
- What will happen if you do a certain test or procedure?
- What will happen if you don't do a certain test or procedure?

In addition to any of these, what questions do you have?

F. What worries or concerns you most? For example, if you're worried about mastectomy recovery, research it and prepare your questions for the doctor. If you're worried about the dangers of radiation, do the same thing. Now make a list of all your questions and prioritize them so you can ask the most important questions first.

As a cancer patient, you are in a problem-solving mode, and lots of problem-solving theories abound. Although it's not my purpose to dissect those, I am suggesting that your problem-solving style affects your cancer treatment. Keep in mind that there is no one right or perfect style, especially considering the numerous types and levels of possible diagnoses and prognoses. It may help you, however, to identify your own best procedure and what helps you best solve problems. Then you can intentionally discern your strategies from there.

G. How would you describe your usual way of solving problems?

H. What can you do to accommodate the ways you think and need to operate to be at peace and feel empowered?

I. Can you think of times you didn't follow through on something until you were satisfied with the answers or results? How do you feel about that now? How can you avoid that scenario in your cancer journey?

Truths to Inspire You

Earlier you read my first blog, "When Eagles Fly." I wrote it at our lake cabin when a fierce storm arose, bending trees and crashing waves into the rocky harbor. Usually our property is teeming with birds, but they were noticeably absent as the storm surged, except for the bald eagles. They glided, dove, and soared with ease. Besides wishing I were an eagle right then, I wondered why they seemed to relish the storm. Although I knew nothing about their abilities, I could see they were confident to handle whatever that storm had to offer. As I imagined the eagles saying, "I have the wings for this," I made the analogy to cancer.

Since then, I've discovered some facts that confirm my conclusions about eagles in storms:

- Eagles use thermal (warm air currents) or dynamic (wind gradient or gusts) soaring techniques. The idea is that they fly directly into the currents where air flows rapidly over their wings and propels them upward to soar and glide.
- Eagles alternate soaring high with swooping downward to catch their next lift.
- Eagles use the pressure of the storm to their advantage.
- When eagles soar together, they are called a "kettle" of eagles.
- Mature bald eagles have a wingspan of about six to eight feet and approximately seven thousand feathers that are lightweight, strong, and highly flexible.
- Feathering configuration enables them to increase or reduce drag as required.
- Their feathers insulate them from cold and heat by trapping layers of air. To maintain a comfortable temperature, they simply change the position of their feathers.

Applying these attributes metaphorically to cancer, we assert:

- We are made to fly above the storm.

- We can let a storm take us down or we can learn how and when to turn into it and go higher.
- Soaring high takes less energy than flapping continuously at low altitudes.
- We can use the pressure to our advantage.
- Storms often come in surges. We need to read the cancer storm to know when to confront or ride it.
- When we soar with others, we create a special bond.
- Power comes from being light, strong, and flexible—light without anxiety, strong from inner resolve, and flexible to bend toward and with the wind.
- We can slow down and come to a stop when necessary or desired.
- When at rest, we can reposition ourselves to achieve optimum physical well-being.

J. What will give you wings to weather the cancer storm?

At my first book sale, a fifteen-year-old boy and his mom stopped by my booth. She told me he had just completed his last chemo. Without hesitation, I leaned toward him and said, "Good for you. You are on your way now into your future. Go ahead and dream about what you want that to look like." He listened, locked his eyes with mine, and his mom cried. I felt an immediate connection with him, respect for what he had endured, and hope for his future. There was a dignity about him that I will never forget. His mom was proud of him, and so was I.

K. Select one possible future goal to motivate you during your treatment. For example, more time with your family, visiting a foreign country, or accomplishing something you've put off for years.

Think about what it will be like to say, "I'm a survivor." When I make that statement, I feel a sense of accomplishment, gratitude, empathy, compassion, determination, energy, and strength. I was talking to another survivor once who said to me, "If I were given the choice whether or not to have cancer, in retrospect, I would choose to have it." Since I've written two books about honesty in the cancer journey, I have to say I would not make that choice. But I can affirm that I am content and happy with how I chose to fight cancer. I can own that attitude with confidence, and I'm writing this book to help you dream for and work toward your own victory.

L. What will make you proud of how you chose to fight cancer?

Truths to Discover

How would you draw or describe the cancer storm in your life? What is noticeably absent? Noticeably present?

Now insert yourself into the scene. Are you an observer, in the midst, above, beneath? Detached or engaged?

Choices for the Journey—Make a Plan

The following choices are time-specific suggestions, but select only what appeals to you, or write your own in any order you prefer.

Today: I will research and find accurate information about my diagnosis.

This week: I will prepare questions for my doctors ahead of time.

This month: I will be a proactive patient.

Long term: I will advocate for my health without shame or embarrassment.

New Mindset for Selecting Treatment

Summarize your most significant take-away concept from this chapter.

Meditation

Take time to imagine, relax, and rest. Feel free to write your thoughts as they come to you.

Possible free-association words:

- Wings
- Storm
- Strength

Feed your fears and your faith will starve.
Feed your faith, and your fears will.[10]

Max Lucado

Chapter Four

Settle Faith and Mortality Issues

Cancer Requires an Answer— What Do You Really Believe?

Truths to Free You

Not everyone believes in God or believes as others do. I get that. My purpose isn't to delve into a bunch of theology. But I am a faith person, and the only way I could deal with mortality was through that perspective. Whatever your beliefs are, however, you can still apply the basic principles addressed in this chapter.

Mortality is a tough subject. When we realize that mortality applies to us, it hits us hard. As I've often said and written, I got the memo. At some point as cancer patients, we slam into that realization. When I dealt with it, my knees hit the ground.

So why deal with mortality at all? Is that necessary?

Some may not think so, but from my own experience and that of others who have shared their journeys with me, cancer is a perfect time to face our mortality and settle once and for all what we really believe, especially about an afterlife.

Depending on our faith system, we can view mortality in a number of ways. A wall with no doors. A horror to be endured. An unknown to be feared. A transition to eternal life. A victory to culminate our existence. A simple ending. How we view mortality is as varied as we humans are.

When we receive the cancer diagnosis, our immediate thoughts take off like horses on a racetrack, and we have no idea which one will cross the finish line first. But the finish line becomes the focus as we ask these questions:

How far along is the cancer?

Am I dying? How long do I have?

What's going to happen to me? Will I suffer?

What does my future hold? Do I even have a future?

A. How do you view mortality? What thoughts or questions do you have about it?

For me, just two days before my deadline to submit my treatment selections, I was still perplexed. I felt as though I had portaged to a deep river with raging rapids and the only options involved a limited number of rafts, all of which had something wrong with them. At that point I realized I had to accept my mortality, and it wasn't easy. Backed into an emotional corner, I prayed gut-level prayers that surprised me, but it was worth it. I would never have anticipated the positive change of heart I experienced.

Myth #11: I should never doubt faith or God.

Myth #12: Strong people, especially spiritual ones, are never afraid.

B. "Never" is a big word, isn't it? What are the lies we believe in Myths #11 and #12?

C. Chances are, if you've not dealt honestly with the prospect of death before, you have some type of negative emotion connected with it. Whatever your situation, describe any obstacles that block your peace about mortality.

D. Write your own Truths #11 and #12.

Truths to Empower You

Let's revisit the airplane cockpit image I described in the introduction. Imagine trying to fly that jet plane with no air traffic controller in a tower. Personally, I saw myself as the pilot of my cancer treatment with God as the air traffic controller. He had the radar for the big picture and the power to coordinate my takeoff, flight pattern, landing, and everything in between. Since powerlessness rides tandem with a cancer diagnosis, I knew I needed divine intervention and support to back me up because, like it or not, I was responsible to pilot the plane.

As for your own journey, how do you see God's part in all of this? I respectfully suggest you find a good answer to that question, because:

- You don't know everything.
- Your life is at stake.
- You're facing a brutal disease.
- You can't control the future.

I acknowledge that these points are blunt, but by now you are well aware of the war you're in, the stakes involved, and how much you want to win it. To do so, you must confront, accept, and even embrace the hardest realities of life, some of which include the possibility of dying. Some of you have advanced-stage cancer. That doesn't mean you won't make it, because I've met stage-4 people who are still here. But it does mean mortality is relevant.

According to the National Comprehensive Cancer Network, "Experts say that spiritual or religious practices can help you adjust to the effects of cancer and its treatment. Patients who rely on their faith or spirituality tend to experience increased hope and optimism, freedom from regret, higher satisfaction with life, and feelings of inner peace."[11]

That's an impressive list of benefits, certainly worthy of consideration. In fact, we could make a good case that patients like those in the previous quotation are empowered patients. With that in mind, let's take a further look at spirituality and how you view your own faith.

E. How do you see God in all of this?

F. What do you believe happens after death? How does your belief about the afterlife affect your cancer journey?

G. Have you wondered why you got cancer? Before you answer, consider this: Even if you have lifestyle habits to change, you didn't deserve cancer. No one does. If you want to make changes in your life, commit to doing so and move on. Guilt or regrets might motivate, but they won't heal you.

H. What questions do you have for God?

Myth #13: What did I do wrong to deserve cancer?

I. Write your own Truth #13.

Truths to Inspire You

When I got to this point in my cancer journey, dealing with mortality, I just wanted peace. Peace about my treatment options. Peace about the future. Peace about cancer and what to believe. In the first month in particular, my days were packed with a frenzy of doctor visits, gathering data, decisions, communicating with loved ones, and reeling from the shock that the "C word" was now officially attached to me. In order to find that peace, I had to search hard for it.

As a Christian, I had always believed that heaven was real. But that's easy to do when your health is good. When I faced cancer, I was stunned at the prospect of dying. Mortality had never shown up on my radar before. If that's not an issue for you, I'm glad; but if it is, I'm glad for you as well. Sooner or later we all need to find solid footing on these beliefs. My search produced a clearer vision of my future on earth and beyond death. With that vision intact, I was better positioned to focus on my healing.

At this point you might be thinking, "I'm too tired" or "Really, on top of everything else, you want me to focus on mortality?" Yes, because as I quoted in chapter one, putting aside emotions during treatment can likely lead to emotional ups and downs, even depression during survivorship. Certainly that prospect is not part of your dreams for the future. As tough as this is, you will be glad later, not only when you approach survivorship but also for the rest of your time on this earth. Simply put, you will enjoy life more.

J.   What brings you peace? What gives you joy?

In an October 2015 study published in *Cancer*, a peer-reviewed journal of the American Cancer Society online, lead author Dr. Heather Jim of the Moffitt Cancer Center in Tampa, Florida, wrote that patients with higher levels of spiritual well-being reported better physical health. Additionally the researchers found that religion and spirituality can help patients find meaning and comfort. The report comprised several research studies of more than 32,000 patients.[12]

K. What beliefs in your faith will help you find better physical health, meaning, and comfort?

L. What are your spiritual goals?

Truths to Discover

I love dogs. My parents owned a dog kennel, and I worked in it while growing up. My siblings and I like to joke we were raised by a golden retriever.

Years ago in a magazine, I read a woman's letter to Dr. Billy Graham to ask if her dog would be in heaven. His answer (as I remember it): "If heaven would not be heaven without your dog, then your dog will be there." What a lovely and loving response!

How do you envision heaven?

Choices for the Journey—Make a Plan

The following choices are time-specific suggestions, but select only what appeals to you, or write your own in any order you prefer.

Today: I will spend some time with God and be honest.

This week: I will clarify my beliefs about mortality and afterlife.

This month: I will actively seek and do things that bring me peace.

Long term: I will make my spiritual welfare a priority.

New Mindset to Settle Matters of Faith and Mortality

Summarize your most significant take-away concept from this chapter.

Meditation

Take time to imagine, relax, and rest. Feel free to write your thoughts as they come to you.

Possible free-association words:
- Heaven
- Forever
- God

Attitude is a little thing that
makes a big difference.[13]

Zig Ziglar

Chapter Five

Gear Up for Treatment

Focus—Give It All You've Got

Truths to Free You

How much do you want cancer gone from your body? I mean, really want it. Your determination affects how you engage in treatment and commit to your process.

Years ago, as a young homeowner, I had no idea how to landscape or care for our yard. Among the shrubs we inherited was an ugly, bare-branched wonder that I couldn't wait to eliminate. So on garbage pickup day, I decided to uproot the eyesore and quickly toss it to the curb, or so I thought. Of course, the shrub and its roots resisted, and a battle ensued. I dug, I yanked, and I cranked on those bedraggled branches until I got myself all sweaty and dirty. Meanwhile, I could hear the whirring and clanking of the garbage truck one street away. Then my shrub war turned even uglier. I won't quote myself, because it wasn't pretty.

The next thing I knew, a stocky guy with a big smile was standing at the curb. "I don't know what you want to do, lady," he said, "but whatever it is, you want it real bad."

"I hate this shrub, and you're right. I want it gone real bad."

"Okay," he said. In less than a minute, muscle man was tossing my stubborn old shrub in the grinder. Mission accomplished.

Can we agree that cancer deserves its demise? Think of treatment as a means to dump the cancer where it belongs. You can get the process underway and just so far, but at some point you need a lot of help to get your mission accomplished.

Myth #14: Cancer treatment is a necessary evil.

Let's be frank about treatment options. For me, they all sounded terrible. Not one of them seemed better than

68

any other, and the potential side effects were daunting. As I deliberated about options, the data darted across my brain like Ping-Pong balls. In the end, though, I decided that the side effects were nothing in comparison to untreated cancer.

A. What is your attitude going into treatment? Are you confident? Determined? Ready to give it everything you've got?

B. Which of these statements most closely match your own beliefs about your treatments? Be honest. This is the time to identify and acknowledge your beliefs—before you actually begin your treatments.
   - Opportunities to embrace—I'm as ready as I can be.
   - Miserable options but the best available—I've decided what to do, but I feel cornered.
   - Vague and questionable options—I'm not sure about any of it.
   - Risky choices but worth it—I know it's hard, but I'm determined.
   - Battle strategies for victory—I'm grateful for the chance to live.

Do you have other beliefs about your treatments?

C. Including those you just wrote in item B, list the statements that apply to you from highest to lowest priority. Don't filter or default to what you think you should write.

Are you peaceful with your list? If not, you can choose what to emphasize. Rearrange your priority list and write it on the other side of the index card you're using for a bookmark (chapter one, Truths to Inspire You, item A.)

Once your course is set, I recommend planning ahead. Become as informed as possible about the schedule and any procedural details that may arise because, I assure, you there are lots of small decisions to be made on the actual days of treatment. If you know what those could be ahead of time, you will avoid unnecessary stress.

D. Write your own Truth #14.

Truths to Empower You

Tomer T. Levin M.D. wrote an online article for *Psychology Today* citing the differences between a "prehab" and "rehab" mentality toward cancer. The rehab mindset says, "Let's finish the treatment and then we'll strengthen your body." Conversely, Levin says, a prehab mindset begins soon after diagnosis, views the treatment period as a proactive "pathway to wellness,"[14] and includes creative physical, work, and psychological components. For example, he recommended that you "ask your oncologist to order physical therapy from the get-go."[15] In retrospect, I wish I had heard that tip when I was newly diagnosed.

If all of that sounds too ambitious or optimistic to you, Levin also warned against over-optimistic expectations. "My suggestion," he writes, "is to approach prehab with realistic optimism and a spirit of gentle experimentation. Test what works and what needs to be tweaked. Taken in a measured dose, the prehab mindset is an adaptive approach to physical activity, work, and maintaining your spirits in the face of cancer."[16]

Regarding your treatment, think about the mindsets you want to adopt for the days ahead, and understand that you alone can and have a right to decide what those will be. Compare and combine the best options, advice, and practical ideas you can find. Obviously, you can't control all aspects of treatment or its results, but your mindsets and attitudes have an impact on the course of events. If you will be objective and imaginative for a few minutes, you can map out how you want to lead this incredibly valuable person—you—through cancer.

When treatment ends, what will make you proud of how you navigated this journey? When you've answered that question, you will know how to mentally engage in your treatment process.

    E. What activities will help you adopt a prehab mindset toward physical activity? Work? Maintaining your spirits during treatment?

F. Knowing your own personality and needs, how can you gently experiment with prehab activities?

G. Write a sentence that summarizes your realistic optimism toward cancer.

Truths to Inspire You

During treatment, the greatest test of my perseverance happened in the radiation room. Although I had accepted the dangers of radiation, as I lay on the hard, flat table, I felt alone and anxious. Thankfully, the hard table helps patients hold still during treatment. But I was still nervous and feared that I would move slightly, allowing the beams to miss their mark and damage my organs.

Desperate for a solution, I wanted to redirect my attention during radiation in the subsequent days and weeks. In retrospect, I am grateful because now I can help you prepare for those moments. For you, the answer could be anything from a song to a favorite memory. For me, because of my faith and perhaps you would do this as well, I chose a Scripture, Psalm 103:1–5, which was significant during my diagnosis period.

The next day—anchoring my right hand on my waistband, willing my muscles to be still, and stretching my left arm overhead—I closed my eyes and quietly recited those verses in my mind. The strategy worked so well I felt relaxed the whole time, and I didn't feel alone. At first

I planned to select other passages for the remaining six weeks, but to my great surprise, that Scripture was more than enough for me every day. In fact, I still set my cell phone alarm for 10:20 a.m. every morning (my daily appointment time for radiation), recite those same verses, and remind myself how grateful I am to be cancer free.

Myth #15: Treatment is always lonely and miserable, and there's nothing I can do about that.

    H. Do you have a favorite book? Quotation? Scripture? Song? What do you want to focus on during treatment?

Myth #16: During the treatment period, I won't be able to enjoy normal activities.

    I. Cancer interrupts our normal life and schedule. There's no way to avoid that. But if we adopt the prehab attitude and choose to keep positive and constructive activities, we will benefit physically, mentally, emotionally, psychologically, and spiritually. Select the things you won't neglect or give up during your treatment period.

    J. List anything you want to add to your treatment period. For example, if I had been aware of prehab attitudes, I would have added a spa massage or two not only to relax but also to reward myself. Wouldn't a gift certificate to a spa be a great gift from friends and family?

K. Write your own Truths #15 and #16.

Truths to Discover

For me, treatment options seemed like whitewater rafts with structural issues. You, however, might love whitewater rafting. So how would you describe or draw the treatment options available to you? Note that I selected an image with lots of people in my raft, which confirms my conviction to involve others, including my medical team, in my journey. I also envisioned myself as the one standing and steering.

One of my favorite feel-good movies is *Secretariat,* a story about a history-making racehorse, also called "Big Red," whose owner and stable team never stopped believing in him. He won the Triple Crown in 1973. Sportswriter Mike Sullivan said:

> *"I was at Secretariat's Derby, in '73. . . . That was . . . just beauty, you know? He started in last place, which he tended to do. I was covering the second-place horse, which wound up being Sham. It looked like Sham's race going into the last turn, I think. The thing you have to understand is that Sham was fast, a beautiful horse. He would have had the Triple Crown in another year. And it just didn't seem like there could be anything faster than that.*

Everybody was watching him. It was over, more or less. And all of a sudden there was this, like, just a disruption in the corner of your eye, in your peripheral vision. And then before you could make out what it was, here Secretariat came. And then Secretariat had passed him. No one had ever seen anything run like that—a lot of the old guys said the same thing. It was like he was some other animal out there.[17]

I love this story. Secretariat had a team of stable workers and trainers to help him, and there was no way he could have done it without them. But when the race was on, he knew how to run it the way he wanted and the way he could win it.

How would you apply that principle to your cancer journey?

Choices for the Journey—Make a Plan

The following choices are time-specific suggestions, but select only what appeals to you, or write your own in any order you prefer.

Today: I will obtain treatment details in advance to minimize surprises and approach treatment with realistic confidence.

This week: I will seek prehab activities that bring me peace, strength, and encouragement.

This month: I will give my treatment period my complete, full-hearted, and best effort.

Long term: When I am a survivor, I will share my experiences openly to help new patients on their journey.

New Mindset for Treatment

Summarize your most significant take-away concept from this chapter.

Meditation

Take time to imagine, relax, and rest. Feel free to write your thoughts as they come to you.

Possible free-association words:
- Optimism
- Focus
- Hope

Stress makes your body more
hospitable to cancer.[18]

Lorenzo Cohen

Chapter Six

Conquer Stress

Stress Is Heavy—Lift, Press, and Release

Truths to Free You

The first month of cancer is major stress on steroids. It's like trying to lift a barbell loaded with weights heavier than you are without any preparation or training beforehand. Moreover, you don't even know where the barbell came from. Suddenly, it's sprawled across your back, stretching from shoulder to shoulder, buckling your knees beneath you. The tension feels as though it literally could break you.

I'm not exaggerating, am I? Personally, I've never wanted to be an expert on stress, and I'm still not an expert. But I've learned different types of stress can have good and/or bad effects on me. When stress helps or motivates me to be productive or overcome obstacles, as long as it's short term without negative emotions, I've found it helpful.

But we are talking about bad stress here—the kind that knots your muscles, disturbs your sleep, gives you headaches, and lingers. By the time I finished treatment, my life looked like a multicar crash on a freeway. The stress was mind boggling. Throughout my experience, I learned a few things:

- Cancer reeks of stress.
- Stress interrupts and sabotages healing.
- Stress tends to multiply during crises.

I don't know why crises pile up the way they do. I've read some theories but, in the final analysis, it's uncannily common, so much so that some hefty research and postulating is out there. Do an internet search sometime.

On the MD Anderson Cancer Center at the University of Texas website, Lorenzo Cohen, PhD, professor of General Oncology and Behavioral Science, says that health experts are still sorting out whether stress actually causes cancer. But they do agree that it can promote and spread some forms of it because "stress makes your body more hospitable to cancer."[19] In that same article, Anil K. Sood, MD, professor of Gynecologic and Reproductive Medicine, differentiates between short-term and long-term stress, saying that the former dissipates when the causative event ceases, but the latter type (ongoing or chronic stress) damages and weakens the immune system. "No-end-in-sight" stress "can help cancer grow and spread in a number of ways," he says, because stress hormones inhibit anoikis, a process that kills diseased cells and keeps them from spreading.[20]

I share this with you to make the point that ongoing stress is verifiably harmful for your cancer journey. Of course, the stresses of cancer are legitimate. But we can't afford to let them overtake us or stake a claim on us 24/7.

As for crises clusters, please understand that if additional crises happen to you on top of the cancer, you're not different, you haven't messed up somehow, and you aren't failing in your cancer journey. You can let the subsequent stress pin you to the mat like a wrestling opponent, or you can strategize your moves and end up on top. But your first defense is to size up the opponent and do whatever is possible to make your body inhospitable to cancer.

A. List the top three to five items that are causing your stress right now. What do these items have in common?

In the introduction, I wrote that you will likely change during the course of your cancer journey. Change of any kind is inherently stressful for most of us. When I sign books, I tell people, "You decide how you want change to look."

B. Have you ever seen how good results or changes trump bad events in the end? How can you convert your current stress from something negative and futile to positive and hopeful change?

The Mayo Clinic website addresses the potential financial stresses of cancer treatment. It says, "Many unexpected financial burdens can arise as a result of a cancer diagnosis. Your treatment may require time away from work or an extended time away from home. Consider the additional costs of medications, medical devices, traveling for treatment and parking fees at the hospital."[21]

Certainly this type of stress is a real-life concern. To deal with it, the Mayo Clinic suggests you ask the following questions of your health care team:

- Will I have to take time away from work?
- Will my friends and family need to take time away from work to be with me?
- Will my insurance pay for these treatments?
- Will my insurance cover the cost of medications?
- How much will my out-of-pocket costs be?
- If insurance won't pay for my treatment, are there assistance programs that can help?
- Do I qualify for disability benefits?
- How does my diagnosis affect my life insurance?[22]

Asking these questions at the onset of diagnosis exemplifies a proactive patient. Cancer is filled with enough surprises. If we can avoid some of those surprises, especially crucial ones such as financial issues, we position ourselves to find solutions and reduce stress. Hospitals and clinics are well aware of potential financial hardships, and many offer resources to help.

C. Do you have financial concerns for treatment? What are they and how do you plan to address them?

How do we handle stress in the cancer journey? We cannot make light of the numerous issues inherent in a disease as life threatening as cancer. But as Dr. Cohen and Dr. Sood warn us, neither can we let stress take hold and keep us constantly upset and anxious. The goal is to keep it from overwhelming us. In addition to the tips I offered in chapter five for handling the anxious moments of treatment, consider these suggestions, also from the Mayo Clinic website:

- Talk to cancer survivors or support groups.
- Connect with the American Cancer Society's Cancer Survivors Network.
- Practice relaxation techniques, exercise, and choose a healthy diet.
- Maintain honest two-way communication with family, friends, a spiritual adviser or counselor.
- When faced with a difficult decision, list the pros and cons for each choice.

- Find a source of spiritual support.
- Set aside time to be alone.
- Remain involved with work and leisure activities as much as you can.[23]

Notice that most of these tips have been covered and applied in the previous chapters of this book. Also, understand stress reduction techniques vary. There is not a one-size-fits-all program. We're all different and highly individual in our life situations and how we react to problems. Listen to your self-talk, body symptoms, and subtle signs that serve to warn you stress is affecting you.

Also, sometimes when we're feeling overwhelmed, we think we have to do something huge or dramatic to overcome the anxiety we feel. But, as I mentioned in the introduction, small steps such as I've described in the Choices for the Journey section are more practical and effective long term.

As for attitude, think about the weight-lifting analogy at the beginning of this chapter. Decide to get rid of the stress by taking a firm position, grabbing hold of it, lifting it up to God, and releasing it.

Myth #17: Stress is unavoidable. It's useless to even try.

D. Review all the suggestions we've listed for combatting stress. Add any of your own and write your Truth #17.

Truths to Empower You

When I was diagnosed, I had just launched a new arts organization that was several years in the making. In fact, we held a successful and well-received seminar the previous weekend, and other major events lay ready for the summer and fall. I could have called it quits, and no one would have blamed me. I decided, however, to leave the schedule intact. I didn't know how it would all come together, but I refused to let cancer derail the project. Having spent a lot of time and energy on that vision, I wanted to finish what I started. I'm not saying it was easy. Determination has its down moments, but I am saying it was worth it.

Meaningful work or purpose is a prerequisite for joy and satisfaction as a human being. I hope you have something like that in your life. If you do, then by all means protect that gift and don't let go of it no matter what cancer may look like now. Purpose empowers, adversity strengthens, and choice moves us forward.

If you don't have meaningful work or a satisfying purpose, why not use this time in your life to change that? Do you know what happens to a butterfly fresh out of a cocoon? The first thing it needs to do is hang upside down to expand and dry its wings. Why? Because it wants to fly. Stress is like that. You feel as though everything is upside down but, in time, your wings will be worth it.

At the time of my diagnosis, a cancer survivor told me she felt as though she had become a member of a club she never wanted to join, adding happily that, as a result, she was much more grateful for life.

I assure you that she was right. All the cancer survivors I know—truly all of them—say the same thing. Life is an amazing privilege. When you finish cancer treatment, you will appreciate every breath and every day as never before.

All things considered, this might be a perfect time to clarify your goals in life and make the changes you've always wanted.

Myth #18: I'll never have a truly productive life again. Why bother with purpose, goals, or vision?

    E. What do you think of Myth #18? If someone said that to you, what would you tell him or her? In other words, what would your Truth #18 be?

In Minneapolis, Minnesota, the I-35W Mississippi River bridge collapsed on August 1, 2007, just at the end of rush hour. Thirteen people died and 145 were injured. A young woman miraculously survived the crash. Immediately afterward, she remembered her dream to teach art to inner city children—a dream she had conceived in college but buried for the practicalities of a career. After her trauma, she found like-minded artists, got a grant, leased a small space in an urban neighborhood, and began to teach not only children but also the surrounding community. Sometimes life's storms take us to heights we never thought possible.

F. Do you have meaningful work or purpose? How can you protect that and keep it intact during your treatment period?

G. If you don't have meaningful work or purpose, let yourself dream. What would you like to do with your life after treatment?

Truths to Inspire You

Stress is like a kaleidoscope. As the barrel of life twists, an orderly design tumbles into temporary disarray. At first the chips scramble into nonsensical directions, but when the scene settles, a rearranged design appears, often just as good or beautiful if not better than the former one.

Can you relate to the word "scramble" right now? By the time I finished treatment, crisis after crisis had scrambled our lives thoroughly. Someone stole Tom's hauling trailer (worth about $20,000, contents included) from his work parking lot. Both Tom and I were in car accidents; fortunately, neither one of us was injured. My office building flooded almost two feet deep from a sewer backup, destroying most of my furniture and records. Last but not least, a water pipe burst in a lower bedroom of our home, saturating the ceiling, walls, furniture, carpet, and closet. All of these events occurred during my diagnosis and treatment period.

When the house flooded, I could definitely say things were about as messed up as I'd ever seen them. But then, one by one, things untangled. Thanks to insurance benefits, Tom got money for the trailer, and I found a wonderful office closer to home. Also, the remodeling of the bedroom turned out to be a much better fit for my grandchildren who stayed there when visiting. Then I got a new and better car. Best of all, my surgery and radiation rendered me cancer free.

Of course, I cannot promise or assure similar or better results for all patients, but I can say that overcoming stress is well worth the effort because it helps you eliminate hormonal hospitality to cancer inside you body. When you free yourself from ongoing negative stress, you set the stage for the best possible outcome from treatment.

Be encouraged. As you envision the days ahead, understand that you can overcome the stresses of cancer. Don't give up or give in to despair. Hold on to your purpose and passions. Will you have to work hard at this? No doubt about it, but stress can be a gateway to change. Make it a positive one.

H. What stress issues did you have before cancer?

I. How would you compare those issues with the ones you're experiencing now?

J. What is your attitude toward stress now? And the role it can play in your journey?

Truths to Discover

How does your kaleidoscope of life look? Orderly? In transition? Unsettled? Complicated? Colorful? Appealing? Interesting? Intricate? Simple?

In this chapter I talked about stress being a gateway to change. Depending on your perspective, such gates vary in size, purpose, and attributes. For example, they can be ornate or basic, solid or translucent, formidable or beautiful. Draw or find an image that represents your perspective on the gates (changes) you face right now. Are they shut, open wide, or slightly open? What lies behind them? How big are they? Inviting or daunting? Don't judge. It is what it is, and that's good to know.

Choices for the Journey—Make a Plan

The following choices are time-specific suggestions, but select only what appeals to you or write your own in any order you prefer.

Today: I will pay attention to my body and mind so as to identify stress as soon as it emerges.

This week: I will take steps to relax and release tension.

This month: I will not allow stress to continue long term in my body.

Long term: I will find meaning in the journey and purpose for my life.

New Mindset for Conquering Stress

Summarize your most significant take-away concept from this chapter.

Meditation

Take time to imagine, relax, and rest. Feel free to write your thoughts as they come to you.

Possible free-association words:
- Crisis
- Frustration
- Attitude

Street smarts are all about survival and safety in the toughest of neighborhoods. That said; let's talk about cancer smarts.

Chapter Seven

Enjoy Your Future

Life After Cancer—Be Cancer Smart

Truths to Free You

Have you ever climbed to the top of a lighthouse or a skyscraper? On ground level, you can't see too far, because your perspective is limited by a flat view of the landscape or nearby obstructions. But after you climb the stairs, your view expands way beyond what you would have thought possible. That's what it's like to reach survivorship.

When my daughter had toddlers, she got a shirt that said, "You can't scare me. I have a two-year-old." As humorous as that is, in a way, that's how it is with survivorship. Things that used to trouble me aren't as powerful as they were, and I feel stronger. Every day, I rejoice at 10:20 a.m. that I don't have cancer.

When treatment ended, I felt proud of my cancer journey. I like the choices I made and feel good about all of it. Now I write to help you climb to the highest level you can reach. That's the rewarding side of the journey.

As for considering the other side of survivorship, please realize the post-treatment period, though often a relief and joy, is not a panacea or state of perfection. Somehow life is always gritty, isn't it? Moreover, physical challenges, even serious negative effects, can evolve from treatment scenarios. For me, although short term, I had to gradually build up my energy level while recuperating from radiation. Then my daily follow-up medication produced arthritis in my fingers. Finding a new prescription was tedious. But we found something that worked better—not perfectly, but better.

Also, survivors often experience concerns about returning to everyday life. Understandably, recurrence of the cancer is the most universal anxiety, but patients have other worries, too. Sometimes they wonder about their jobs and whether their positions could be in jeopardy after a long absence. Relationships can be another issue, because they think people might view or treat them differently. Patients with limited resources might deal with lingering financial problems.

In chapter one I quoted my oncology center's paragraph about post-treatment emotions. I hope the exercises in this guide have already helped you enter survivorship on a more positive footing. But if you experience some anxiety, it's all right. You're human. I have read accounts from survivors who describe periods of sleeplessness and even panic attacks. But you have already identified, expressed, and chronicled your journey in this book. Reread chapter six or any of the other chapters and review the mindsets you composed for each chapter.

Have you ever heard of street smarts? Street smarts are all about survival and safety in the toughest of neighborhoods. That said, let's talk about cancer smarts.

In particular, I want to encourage you to be smart in the following ways:

- Hold onto your health like a pit bull on a mission.
- Make excellent lifestyle, nutrition, and health care choices, especially ensuring that you get bountiful, regular, and satisfying hours of sleep.
- Use common sense and change any bad habit such as smoking or excessive alcohol or sugar consumption.
- Search cancer center survivorship resources or other online organizations for survivorship care plans. Choose one that makes the most sense to you. It should include follow-up information and

appointments, possible side effects to watch for, and preventive measures and activities for health maintenance.

- If you don't receive a treatment summary, ask your oncologist to order one for you. That summary gives you a record to which you can refer or possibly provide to a different health care professional if needed—for example, if you move to another state.

- Keep track of and always schedule annual physicals, checkups, and tests on time without fail.

- Listen to your body. Observe. Pay attention. If something doesn't seem right, take action right away.

- Develop a practical and firm exercise routine that fits your needs and schedule. This is not optional. Exercise is essential not only for physical but also for emotional and mental health.

- Relapse occurs for some people. I hate that as much as anyone, but it happens, providing all the more reason to be vigilant and not take your health for granted.

- Keep this guide as a memorial of your journey. Read it every anniversary to reflect and appreciate how far you have come.

- Do whatever you can to find and interact with positive-minded people who inspire you. Your comrades in life made a huge difference.

- Continue to foster faith and grow spiritually.

A. What is your plan for taking pit-bull care of your health?

In regard to lifestyle choices, I've read a lot about carcinogens and positive and negative lifestyle choices. Frankly, if I daily executed all the advice I've read, I would not have had time to write this book. But a cancer-smarts person faces the facts, deciphers what's relevant, sets priorities, and sticks to them.

B. Some fitness centers and clubs offer classes specifically geared to cancer patients and survivors. How can you schedule your life to include quality exercise?

C. Ongoing supportive relationships enhance our lives for health and hard times. You can find survivorship support through your oncology hospital or some other medical center, church, or community resource. Some centers offer massage, art therapy, or other enhancement programs. What options could you consider?

Inexplicably, setbacks are common in all aspects of life, including disease recovery. Of course, we want everything to go perfectly. But sometimes we must accept, handle, and move past unexpected setbacks.

Myth #19: If I experience setbacks, there's something wrong with me or the way I handled treatment.

> D. Why is this myth wrong? How does it disempower the cancer survivor? Write your own Truth #19.

Like the weather, we change and so do our circumstances in life.

> E. How have you changed since the beginning of your cancer journey?

Truths to Empower You

As you enter the other side of cancer, you will want to enjoy your victory, and well you should. Remember, though, that the cancer war continues, and we have others joining the ranks. I still consider myself a soldier against the enemy.

How can you enjoy your victory and remain vigilant? Here are some tips:

- Be grateful for life. Find a way to express your gratitude every chance you get.

- Hold on to the values and truths that you wrote in this journal.
- Treasure time.
- Focus on what really counts in life—your spirituality, relationships, and purpose.
- Simplify everything. You won't miss the clutter, confusion, and complications.
- Daily reflect, rest, and renew your inner strength and energy.
- Think of yourself as cancer free. I dislike the word "remission," because generally people consider remission to be a temporary and fragile state of health. The implication is that cancer hasn't completed its mission yet but will likely return. Personally, I can't live like that. I don't want to constantly wonder if cancer is coming back. I understand relapse happens. Nobody gets that concept better than a cancer patient or survivor. But how can we greet each new day with a negative, insecure, and pessimistic mindset? I want to enjoy life and believe for the best possible outcome. I tell people I'm cancer free.
- Find a way to support and encourage other cancer warriors coming up behind you.

Do you remember that I called you a hero or heroine in chapter one? One of my goals in writing this book is to prepare you for the moment you complete treatment. I want you to be able to say you are proud of your journey, including the decisions you made, and that you did everything you could to battle cancer. As I mentioned in that same chapter, I disapprove of people saying that someone "lost her battle with cancer." As you and I and every other survivor knows, we have fought and won every battle we could using all the weapons, armor, and strategies available to us within the current continuum of medical knowledge and expertise.

Again, it is worth repeating: When you have completed treatment, you are already a winner and a champion. Moreover, thousands of survivors annually attest to cancer-free success. I sincerely pray you will be among them.

Throughout this journaling guide, you have had opportunities to evaluate cancer myths and write your own truths. I hope one of those truths is that cancer is not in charge of your life. Remember the hijacking metaphor? Now that I've had cancer, I am more aware than ever that I am responsible for being honest, making good decisions, defining truth, clarifying faith, speaking up for myself, turning stresses into opportunities, and making sure I have exciting dreams to follow. As a result, I've designed a book and this guide to help you do the same.

F. Pick out at least three of the eight empowering tips in this section and cite specific ways you can implement them.

G. Review the new mindsets you've written for this journal. What has been most meaningful to you?

Myth #20: I'll never be truly cancer free.

H. Write your own Truth #21.

Truths to Inspire You

Every so often I ask people to dream with me for the demise of cancer. One of my biggest concerns is the fatalism I see in the culture that surrounds us. People seem to think that cancer is bigger and stronger than anything or anyone. It's almost as though cancer has convinced people that it is god, but it's not my God. And I believe that it's coming down someday. It's not indestructible or infallible or omnipotent. It's a disease whose days are numbered, especially with the ongoing and ever-increasing science for prevention and treatment, the passionate support of an army of survivors, and prayers of people like me who believe cancer is not God.

Consequently, my dreams include:

- survivors who are effective, confident, and strong in life and the fight against cancer;
- a culture that supports patients with positive expectations for survival and health;
- a next generation whose only knowledge of cancer is that it used to be terminal.

Do you have children? Grandchildren? Think about your descendants. Wouldn't it be wonderful if the word "cancer" would never be relevant in their world? I am known for saying, "Why not?" So I present a few "why not" questions for you to consider. Why not believe cancer can and will come down? Why not find ways to help educate our culture about the truths regarding cancer? Why not think big and pray for a discovery that counteracts not just cancer but all autoimmune diseases?

Myth #21: A cure for cancer is unlikely.

At this point, I want to interject my Truth #21, because I'm hoping you can think of more examples and use my truth as a starting point:

That is how people used to view lots of diseases such as smallpox, tuberculosis, polio, and AIDS. I believe that researchers can and will discover a cure for cancer. In the meantime, I will do everything I can to counteract the fatalism and myths surrounding cancer in our culture.

I.   Add your own thoughts about a cure for cancer.

J.   Are there any other myths about cancer you have noticed? If so, include your counteracting truth.

Truths to Discover

This is how I see part of my future. The illustration is called "Woman working on laptop on a mountaintop." I love to write and learn. Notice how peaceful it is, the expansive view, the lovely shade tree, and the stream of sunlight.

How do you see your future?

Choices for the Journey—Make a Plan
The following choices are time-specific suggestions, but select only what appeals to you, or write your own in any order you prefer.

Today: I will obtain or review my treatment summary and survivor care plan.

This week: I will use my treatment summary to write a gratitude list for the miracle of survivorship.

This month: I will search for a survivorship center and find other survivors and activities for ongoing support.

Long term: I will support increased prevention awareness and a cure for cancer.

New Mindset for Your Future

Summarize your most significant take-away concept from this chapter.

Meditation

Take time to imagine, relax, and rest. Feel free to write your thoughts as they come to you.

Possible free-association words:
- Future
- Courage
- Adventure

Conclusion

Thank you for using this guide as part of your journey. We are cancer warriors together and, as such, are linked in heart and spirit, no matter the distance or time that might seem to separate us.

Congratulations in advance for successful treatment and joining the ranks of survivors with me.

I believe in miracles.

— Marianne McDonough

Appendix

Note: If you compare this guide with the original text of *8 Steps to Getting Real with Cancer*, you will see that chapters two and six were combined into chapter two in this book. The original book was written for both newly diagnosed patients and their loved ones, whereas this guide was designed to focus on the patients. Also, the myths have been altered or changed to fit the text and flow of *Beating Cancer*.

Myths and Truths

Remember that the truths expressed here are for reference only. Please write your own truths and use my thoughts, if you want, as a springboard for reflection and discussion.

Chapter One

Myth #1: Cancer is so complicated and powerful, we are helpless against it.

Truth # 1: Cancer is complicated but not omnipotent. I can learn how to fight it and find hope knowing that thousands of survivors have paved the way before me.

Myth #2: Inner reflection is unnecessary and a waste of time.

Truth #2: Inner reflection gives me insight and freedom for the days ahead.

Myth #3: I might fall apart or get too emotional, and that would be embarrassing.

Truth #3: Even people who have never had cancer know that cancer is a tough disease. I do not have to be ashamed of how I feel.

Myth #4: I will never be strong or healthy again.

Truth #4: I cannot predict the future. But I can choose my beliefs, take positive action, and engage fully in the healing process.

Chapter Two

Myth #5: Cancer is an automatic death sentence. Why dream for a future that will never happen?

Truth #5: Cancer is life threatening but no longer the automatic death sentence it once was. I choose to hope.

Myth #6: I don't want to burden or impose on anyone.

Truth #6: I can count on people who love me to be bridges over cancer's troubled water, and I can communicate when I must swim the currents myself.

Myth #7: I have to protect my family and loved ones from the truth about what I'm really feeling and going through.

Truth #7: My number one priority is to get well. I am responsible for my own health and must give that objective my first and best attention. People who truly love me want me to do that. They will stand with me.

Chapter Three

Myth #8: I can't make my own decisions. What if I'm wrong?

Truth #8: There is much controversy and disagreement about cancer treatment protocols. My right decision is the one that makes the most sense to me at the time—the one I have carefully discerned with the tools, information, and competent advice I have at my disposal in the here and now of current theories and expertise.

Myth #9: I'm better off keeping my thoughts to myself and doing what I'm told.

Truth #9: In the long run, my best outcome physically

and emotionally will be the result of a decision I believed in enough to fight for.

Chapter Four

Myth #10: I have to be strong and keep my composure all the time.

Truth #10: That goal is unrealistic and unfair. I have cancer. Genuine strength has nothing to do with keeping it together. In fact, often the greatest test of strength is to accept brokenness, start all over, and create a better future.

Myth #11: I should never doubt my faith or God.

Truth #11: Doubt is a temporary door to increased clarity.

Myth #12: Strong people, especially spiritual ones, are never afraid.

Truth #12: Strength is not measured by the absence of emotion but by the presence of determination melded with the grace of God.

Chapter Five

Myth #13: What did I do wrong to deserve cancer?

Truth #13: Guilt is not helpful. No matter what I've done or not done, I don't deserve cancer. What matters is how I proceed from this point forward.

Myth #14: Cancer treatment is a necessary evil.

Truth #14: Cancer treatments give me a chance to beat this hideous disease. I will do whatever is available and possible to achieve that goal. I am grateful.

Myth #15: Treatment is lonely and miserable, and there's nothing I can do about that.

Truth #15: I can adopt a prehab mindset that allows me to plan and seek activities that set me in forward motion on a positive path.

Chapter Six

Myth #16: During the treatment period, I won't be able to enjoy normal activities.

Truth #16: If I am creative, I can find ways to incorporate activities that give me as close to a normal routine as possible.

Myth #17: Stress is unavoidable. It's useless to even try.

Truth #17: Stress is an interior reaction to events and situations in life. I can choose my reactions, maybe not intentionally at first, but certainly in time. Stress cannot force itself on me long term. I have the power to assess stress and transform it into a gateway for positive change.

Myth #18: I'll never have a truly productive life again. Why bother with purpose, goals, or vision?

Truth #18: I refuse to give up. I may have to adjust my life for physical changes. But I can focus on creating a good future for myself.

Chapter Seven

Myth #19: If I experience setbacks, there's something wrong with me or how I handled treatment.

Truth #19: In everyday life, problems or setbacks occur for all us but especially and even more so during health crises such as cancer. My best strategy is to view setbacks as temporary obstacles, not permanent disabilities.

Myth #20: I'll never be truly cancer free.

Truth #20: I will live each day with profound gratitude and optimism. As far as I'm concerned, I am cancer free, and I choose to adopt and maintain that attitude indefinitely. I will create and design my life accordingly.

Myth #21: A cure for cancer is unlikely.

Truth #21: A cure for and prevention of cancer is inevitable if we unite in prayer and faith for its demise. People used to view lots of diseases such as smallpox, tuberculosis, polio, and AIDS as futile. I believe that researchers can and will discover a cure for cancer. In the meantime, I will do everything I can to counteract the fatalism and myths surrounding cancer in our culture.

Choices for the Journey—
Make A Plan

Chapter One

Today: I will take time to reflect on my beliefs about cancer.

This week: I will identify and acknowledge my concerns about cancer.

This month: I will take courage for the cancer journey by respecting who I am and the value of my own life.

Long term: Someday I will gladly listen to and encourage a new cancer patient.

Chapter Two

Today: I will write a list of decisions to make in the next few weeks.

This week: I will ask someone for help when I need it.

This month: I will listen to people I trust and respect. But I will not expect or allow them to take over or make decisions for me.

Long term: I will give myself permission to dream for a positive future.

Chapter Three

Today: I will research and find accurate information about my diagnosis.

This week: I will prepare questions for my doctors ahead of time.

This month: I will be a proactive patient.

Long term: I will advocate for my health without shame or embarrassment.

Chapter Four

Today: I will spend some time with God and be honest.

This week: I will clarify my beliefs about mortality and afterlife.

This month: I will actively seek and do things that bring me peace.

Long term: I will make my spiritual welfare a priority.

Chapter Five

Today: I will obtain treatment details in advance to minimize surprises and approach treatment with realistic confidence.

This week: I will seek prehab activities that bring me peace, strength, and encouragement.

This month: I will give my treatment period my complete, full-hearted, and best effort.

Long term: When I am a survivor, I will share my experiences openly to help new patients on their journey.

Chapter Six

Today: I will pay attention to my body and mind so as to identify stress as soon as it emerges.

This week: I will take steps to relax and release tension.

This month: I will not allow stress to continue long term in my body.

Long term—I will find meaning in the journey and purpose for my life.

Chapter Seven

Today: I will obtain or review my treatment summary

and survivor care plan.

This week: I will use my treatment summary to write a gratitude list for the miracle of survivorship.

This month: I will search for a survivorship center and find other survivors and activities for ongoing support.

Long term: I will support increased prevention awareness and a cure for cancer.

Graphics Attributions

Book Title and Chapter Titles
  Eagle: ©Jganz | Getty Images/iStock Collection

Chapter One
  Hiking Boots and Hand of Hiker | ©Colby Lysne/Dreamstime.com
  Bench in City Park | ©Terriana/Dreamstime.com

Chapter Two
  Couple Holding Hands | ©Vidor Hsu/iStock.com
  Stone Bridge Over River | ©Torky/Dreamstime.com

Chapter Three
  My Eagle | ©Olga Kalinichenko/Dreamstime.com
  Tree in Autumn Storm | ©Tetordres/Dreamstime.com

Chapter Four
  Stairs to Heaven | ©Agawa288/Dreamstime.com
  Horse | ©seamartini/iStock.com
  Old Sleeping Dog | ©Dmccale/Dreamstime .com

Chapter Five
  Baseball Player | ©Photographerlondon/Dreamstime.com
  Sketch of People on a Raft | ©Anton Kubalik/Dreamstime.com

Chapter Six
  Woman with Barbell | ©Viachaslau Rutkouski/Dreamstime.com
  Kaleidoscope | ©Jkerrigan/Dreamstime.com
  Iron Fences | ©Egorovajulia/Dreamstime.com

Chapter Seven
  Skyscraper View | ©Peter Clark/Dreamstime.com
  Woman with Laptop on a Mountain | ©Mike Kiev/Dreamstime.com

Endnotes

1 Oxford Dictionary Online, www.oed.com.

2 "Feelings and Cancer," National Cancer Institute, www.cancer.gov/about-cancer/coping/feelings, August 20,2018.

3 Marianne C. McDonough, "Go Ahead and Dream," www.8stepstogettingrealwithcancer.com, 2016.

4 "Coping Checklist for Patients," American Cancer Society, www.cancer.org/treatment/treatments-and-side-effects/emotional-side-effects/coping-checklist-for-patients.html.

5 "Coping Checklist for Patients," American Cancer Society, www.cancer.org/treatment/treatments-and-side-effects/emotional-side-effects/coping-checklist-for-patients.html.

6 Marianne C. McDonough, "When Eagles Fly," www.8stepstogettingrealwithcancer.com, 2016.

7 Dr. Jarrod Sheatsley, "Why It's Important to be Honest with Your Doctor," Novant Health, www.novanthealth.org/home/about-us/newsroom/healthy-headlines/articleid/203/why-its-important-to-be-honest-with-your-doctor.aspx, Aug 24, 2015.

8 Dr. Jarrod Sheatsley, "Why It's Important to be Honest with Your Doctor," Novant Health, www.novanthealth.org/home/about-us/newsroom/healthy-headlines/articleid/203/why-its-important-to-be-honest-with-your-doctor.aspx, August 24, 2015.

9 Rosemary Catallo, "Newly Diagnosed Cancer Patients: Questions to Ask Your Health Care Team," MD Anderson Cancer Center, www.mdanderson.org/publications/cancerwise/2013/06/newly-diagnosed-cancer-patients-questions-to-ask-your-health-car.html, June 26, 2013.

10 Max Lucado, *Fearless: Imagine Your Life Without Fear*, Thomas Nelson, Inc., page 155, 2015.

11 National Cancer Comprehensive Network, www.nccn.org/patients/resources/life_with_cancer/spirituality.aspx.

12 Dr. Heather Jim, *Cancer*, a peer-reviewed journal of the American Cancer Society, www.cancer.org/latest-news/study-cancer-patients-with-strong-religious-or-spiritual-beliefs-report-better-health.html, October 21, 2015.

13 Zig Ziglar, *See You at the Top*, Segment Five: Attitude: Chapter One, Quote Page 204, Pelican Publishing Company, Gretna, Louisiana, 1977.

14 Tomer T. Levin M.D., "Prehab vs Rehab Mindsets for People with Cancer," www.psychologytoday.com/us/blog/de-stressing-cancer-and-illness/201711/prehab-vs-rehab-mindsets-people-cancer, November 12, 2017.

15 Tomer T. Levin M.D., "Prehab vs Rehab Mindsets for People with Cancer," www.psychologytoday.com/us/blog/de-stressing-cancer-and-illness/201711/prehab-vs-rehab-mindsets-people-cancer, November 12, 2017.

16 Tomer T. Levin M.D., "Prehab vs Rehab Mindsets for People with Cancer," www.psychologytoday.com/us/blog/de-stressing-cancer-and-illness/201711/prehab-vs-rehab-mindsets-people-cancer, November 12, 2017.

17 *Harper's Magazine*, harpers.org/archive/2002/10/horseman-pass-by, September 18, 2018.

18 Markham Heid, "How Stress Affects Cancer Risk," quoting Lorenzo Cohen, PhD, MD Anderson Cancer Center, www.mdanderson.org/publications/focused-on-health/december-2014/how-stress-affects-cancer-risk.html, December, 2014.

19 Markham Heid, "How Stress Affects Cancer Risk," quoting Lorenzo Cohen, PhD, MD Anderson Cancer Center, www.mdanderson.org/publications/focused-on-health/december-2014/how-stress-affects-cancer-risk.html, December, 2014.

20 Markham Heid, "How Stress Affects Cancer Risk," quoting Anil K. Sood, MD, MD Cancer Center, www.mdanderson.org/publications/focused-on-health/december-2014/how-stress-affects-cancer-risk.html, December 2014.

21 "Cancer Diagnosis: 11 Tips for Coping," Mayo Clinic, www.mayoclinic.org/diseases-conditions/cancer/in-depth/cancer-diagnosis/art-20044544, September 7, 2017. Used with permission of Mayo Foundation for Medical Education and Research. All rights reserved.

22 "Cancer Diagnosis: 11 Tips for Coping," Mayo Clinic, www.mayoclinic.org/diseases-conditions/cancer/in-depth/cancer-diagnosis/art-20044544, September 7, 2017. Used with permission of Mayo Foundation for Medical Education and Research. All rights reserved.

23 "Cancer Diagnosis: 11 Tips for Coping," Mayo Clinic, www.mayoclinic.org/diseases-conditions/cancer/in-depth/cancer-diagnosis/art-20044544, September 7, 2017. Used with permission of Mayo Foundation for Medical Education and Research. All rights reserved.

CPSIA information can be obtained
at www.ICGtesting.com
Printed in the USA
FFHW011251180419
51865936-57261FF

9 780996 697736